Easy Listening

for Keyboards

D1549411

Exclusive Distributors:
Music Sales Limited
8/9 Frith Street,
London W1V 5TZ,
England.
Music Sales Pty Limited
120 Rothschild Avenue,
Rosebery, NSW 2018,
Australia.

Order No. AM92579
ISBN 0-7119-4656-6
ight 1995 by Wise Publications

Compiled by Peter Evans and Peter Lavender
Music arranged by Peter Lavender
Book design by Studio Twenty, London

Printed in the United Kingdom by
Caligraving Limited,
Thetford, Norfolk.

Your Guarantee of Quality
As publishers, we strive to produce every book
to the highest commercial standards.
This book has been carefully designed to minimise awkward
page turns and to make playing from it a real pleasure.
Particular care has been given to specifying acid-free,
neutral-sized paper made from pulps which have not been
elemental chlorine bleached. This pulp is from farmed
sustainable forests and was produced with
special regard for the environment.
Throughout, the printing and binding have been
planned to ensure a sturdy, attractive publication
which should give years of enjoyment.
If your copy fails to meet our high standards,
please inform us and we will gladly replace it.

Music Sales' complete catalogue describes thousands of titles
and is available in full colour sections by subject, direct from
Music Sales Limited. Please state your areas of interest and
send a cheque/postal order for £1.50 for postage to:
Music Sales Limited, Newmarket Road,
Bury St. Edmunds, Suffolk IP33 3YB.

Wise Publications
London/New York/Paris/Sydney/Copenhagen/Madrid

S.95

Guide to ABC & SFX Music

In ABC and SFX music, the melody is clearly written in large lettered notes. Each note can easily be located on your keyboard and then played with the right hand.

The songs in ABC and SFX music books are all written in the following keyboard range. The symbol at the beginning of the music staff is the treble clef, indicating the notes are played with the right hand:

The Keyboard

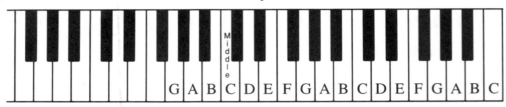

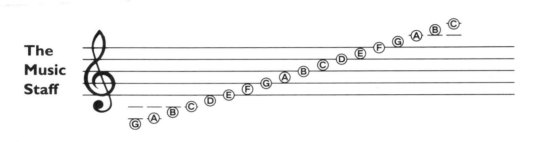

The Sharp Sign (♯) will sometimes appear before a music note. Simply play the *black key* to the *right* of the *white key:*

The Flat Sign (♭) placed before a note tells you to play the *black key* that lies to the *left* of the *white key:*

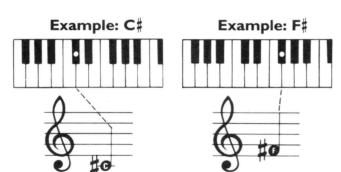

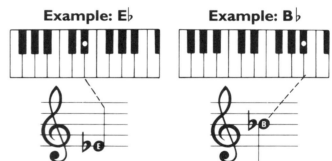

The Music Staff is divided into equal sections by vertical lines called *Bar Lines*. Each section is a *Bar* or *Measure*.

The end of a piece of music is marked by a double bar line.

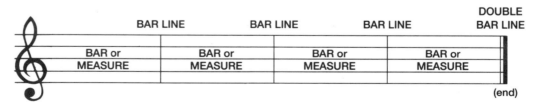

All music is played in time to a *beat*. The six types of notes most often used in

ABC and SFX music all have a *time value* that relates to the beat:

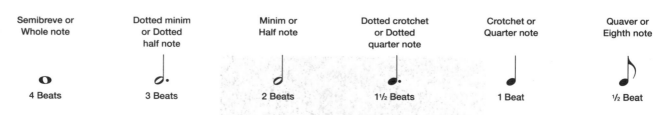

Semibreve or Whole note	Dotted minim or Dotted half note	Minim or Half note	Dotted crotchet or Dotted quarter note	Crotchet or Quarter note	Quaver or Eighth note
4 Beats	3 Beats	2 Beats	1½ Beats	1 Beat	½ Beat

The Rest is a silent break in the music. The symbols are written in the staff, and like music notes, rests each have a time value:

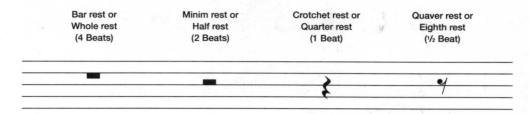

| Bar rest or Whole rest (4 Beats) | Minim rest or Half rest (2 Beats) | Crotchet rest or Quarter rest (1 Beat) | Quaver rest or Eighth rest (½ Beat) |

The Time Signature comprises two numbers at the beginning of the music, after the treble clef sign. The top number shows the amount of beats in each bar or measure.

The bottom number indicates the type of note that will receive *one* beat. These are the most popular time signatures. The lower number 4 represents the crotchet or quarter note:

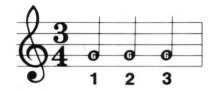

The Tie is a curved line that connects two consecutive notes on the same line or in the same space in the staff. When a tie appears in the music, play the first note and sustain the sound for the *total* time value of the two notes:

Tied Notes

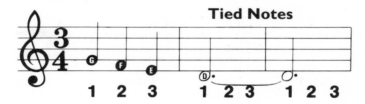

Repeat Signs are two dots alongside double bar lines. They indicate that all the music in between the pairs of repeat signs is to be played through again:

Quite often there will only be one repeat sign at the end of a passage of music. The repeat is then made from the very beginning:

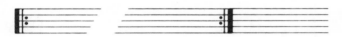

Double Endings are sections of music with staff repeat signs. 1st and 2nd time brackets above the staff indicate where a short 'skip' is to be made in the music after the repeat has been played:

Left Hand Keyboard Accompaniment.
ABC and SFX music has Major and Minor chords clearly written above the staff. The optional 'seventh' type of chord is shown with the 7 outside the chord frame:

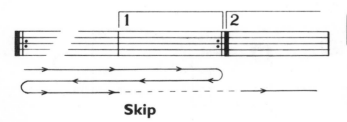

Skip

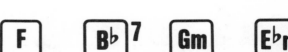

Your Keyboard Owner's Manual will explain how these chords are played with your left hand.

Conventional (Fingered) Chords can also be used. The **Master Chord Chart** in this book shows the most practical chord positions for this type of left hand accompaniment.

Right Hand Fingering
Always use recommended fingering when indicated in ABC/SFX music.

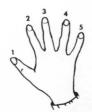

Amazing Grace

Traditional
© Copyright 1995 Dorsey Brothers Music Limited, 8/9 Frith Street, London W1.
All Rights Reserved. International Copyright Secured.

Registration: Oboe or Bagpipes
Rhythm: Waltz
Tempo: Medium Slow

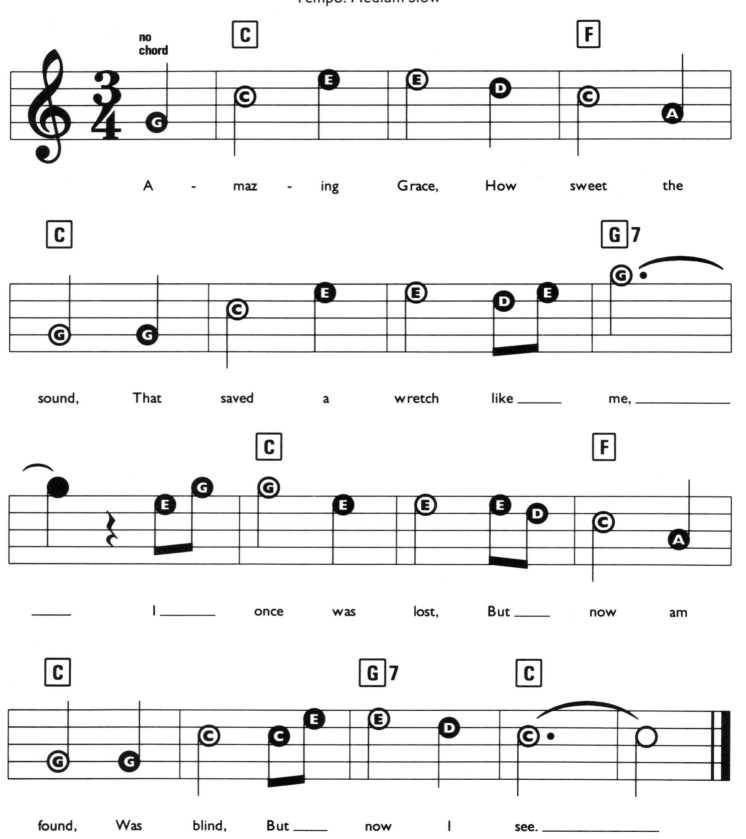

4

Do You Want To Know A Secret?

Words & Music by John Lennon & Paul McCartney

Registration: Saxophone or Piano
Rhythm: Rock
Tempo: Medium

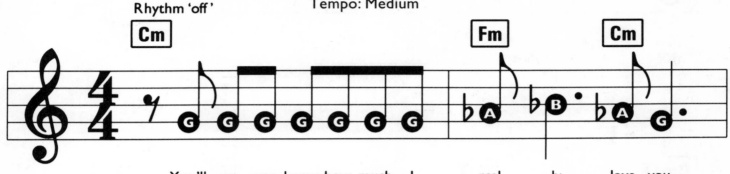

You'll ne - ver know how much I real - ly love you,

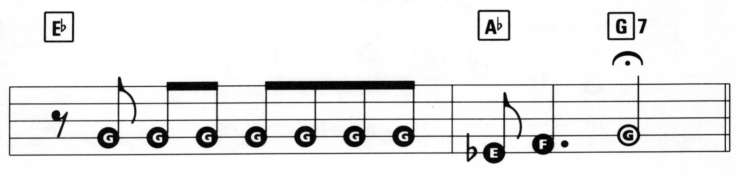

You'll ne - ver know how much I real - ly care.

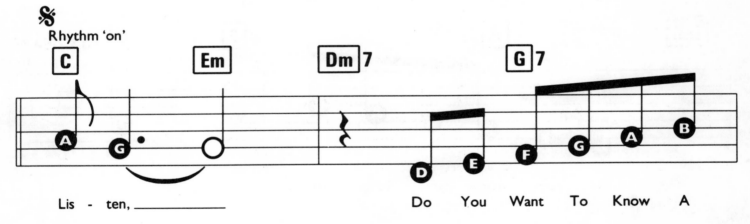

Lis - ten, _____ Do You Want To Know A

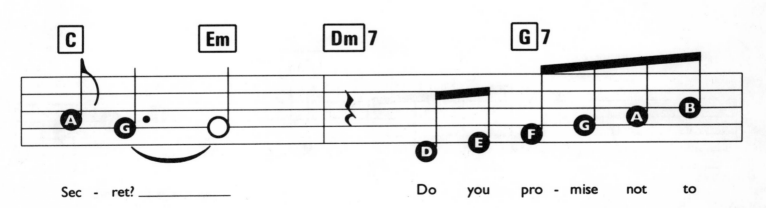

Sec - ret? _____ Do you pro - mise not to

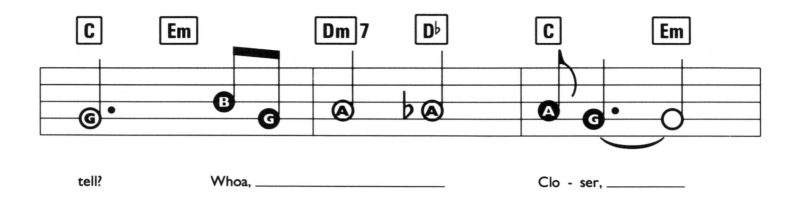

tell?   Whoa, _____   Clo - ser, _____

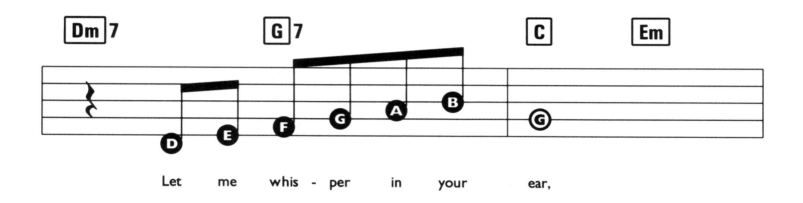

Let   me   whis - per   in   your   ear,

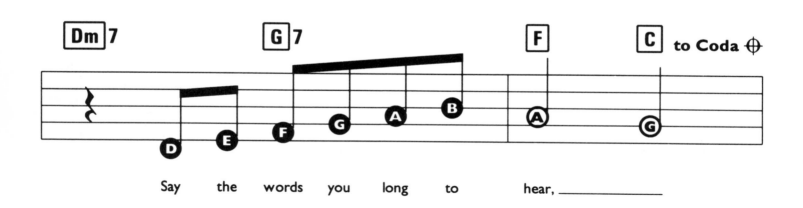

to Coda

Say   the   words   you   long   to   hear, _____

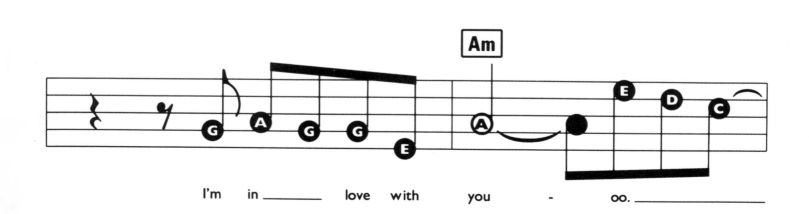

I'm   in _____ love   with   you   -   oo. _____

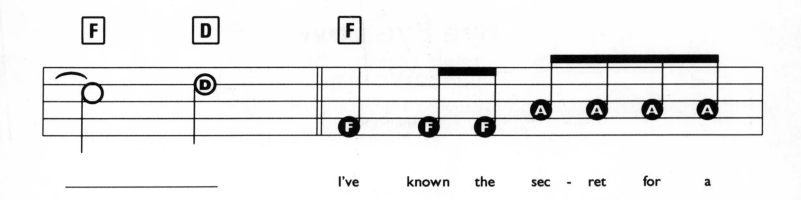

_____ I've known the sec - ret for a

week or two, ____ No - bo - dy knows, Just we two. _____

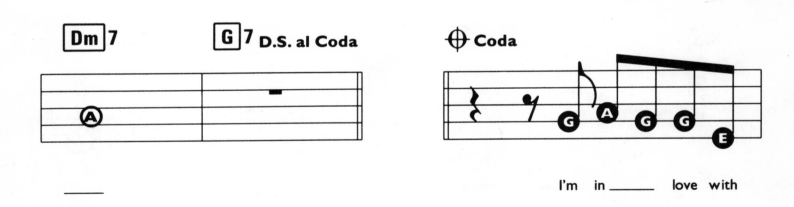

____ I'm in ____ love with

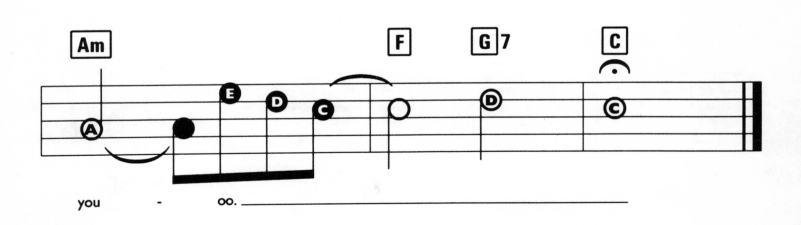

you - oo. _____

Bye Bye Love

Words & Music by Felice & Boudleaux Bryant
© Copyright 1957 House Of Bryant Publications, USA.
Acuff-Rose Music Limited, London W1.
All Rights Reserved. International Copyright Secured.

Registration: Trumpet or Piano
Rhythm: Rock
Tempo: Medium Fast

There goes my ba - by, _____ With some - one
ro - mance, _____ I'm through with

new. _____ She sure looks hap - py, _____ I sure am
love. _____ I'm through with count - ing, _____ The stars a -

blue. _____ She was my ba - by, _____ Till he stepped
bove. _____ And here's the rea - son, _____ That I'm so

in. _____ Good - bye to ro - mance, _____ That might have
free. _____ My lov - in' ba - by _____ Is through with

8

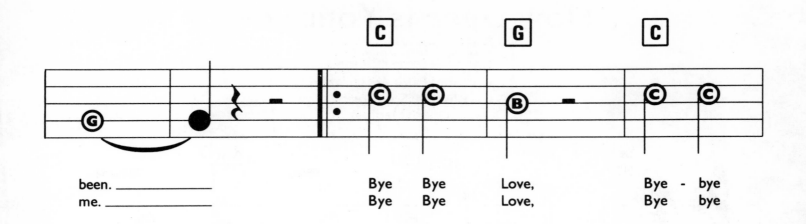

been. _____

me. _____

Bye   Bye   Love,   Bye - bye

Bye   Bye   Love,   Bye bye

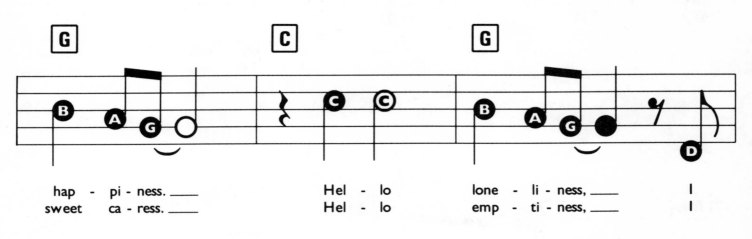

hap - pi - ness. ___   Hel - lo   lone - li - ness, ___   I

sweet ca - ress. ___   Hel - lo   emp - ti - ness, ___   I

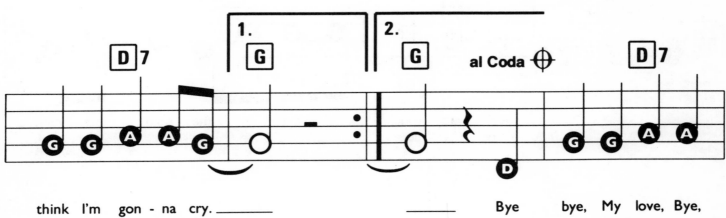

think I'm gon - na cry. _____   ___   Bye   bye, My love, Bye,

feel like I could die. _____

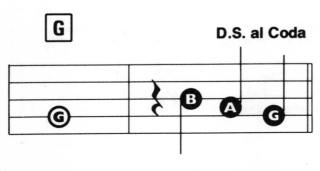

bye.   I'm through with

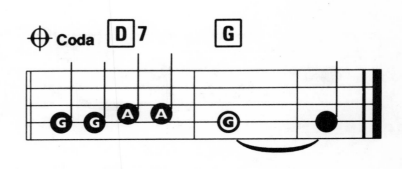

bye, my love, Bye,   bye. _____

How Deep Is Your Love

Words & Music by Barry Gibb, Robin Gibb & Maurice Gibb
© Copyright 1977 Gibb Brothers Music.
All Rights Reserved. International Copyright Secured.

Registration: Flute or Vibraphone
Rhythm: Soft Rock
Tempo: Medium

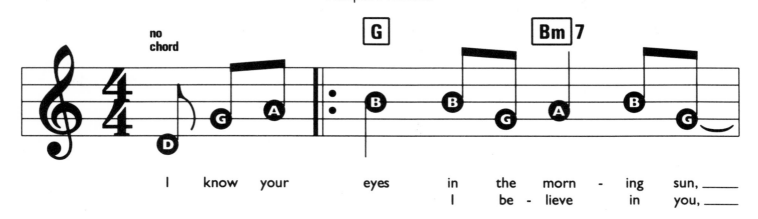

I know your eyes in the morn - ing sun, _____
I be - lieve in you, _____

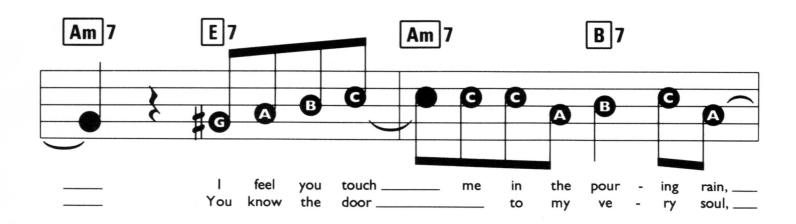

_____ I feel you touch _____ me in the pour - ing rain, _____
_____ You know the door _____ to my ve - ry soul, _____

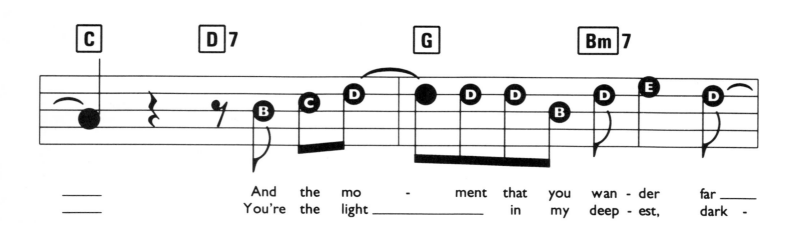

_____ And the mo - ment that you wan - der far _____
_____ You're the light _____ in my deep - est, dark -

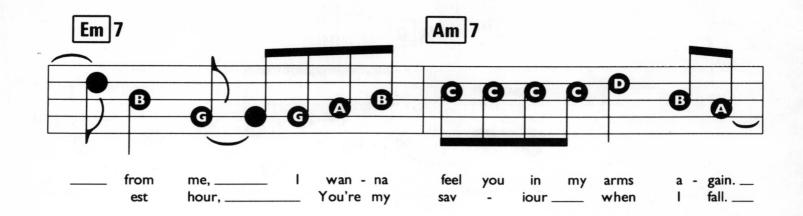

from me, _____ I wan - na feel you in my arms a - gain. ___
est hour, _____ You're my sav - iour ____ when I fall. ___

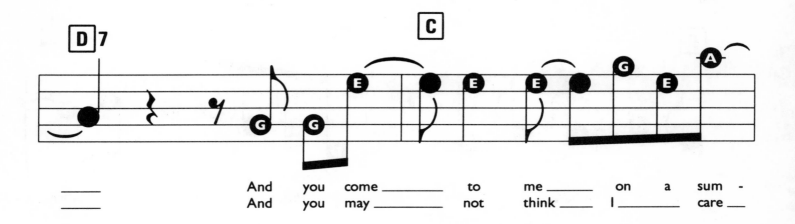

_____ And you come _____ to me _____ on a sum -
_____ And you may _____ not think ____ I _____ care

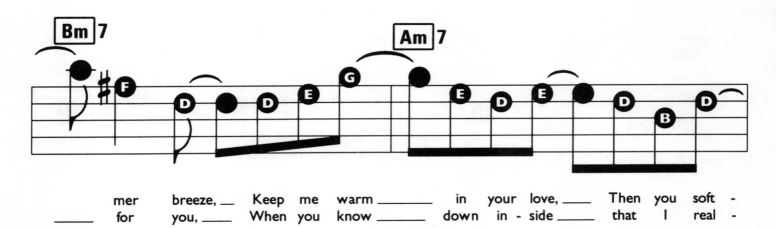

mer breeze, ___ Keep me warm _____ in your love, ___ Then you soft -
_____ for you, ___ When you know _____ down in - side _____ that I real -

ly leave. ___ } And it's me you need ____ to show. ___
ly do. ___ }

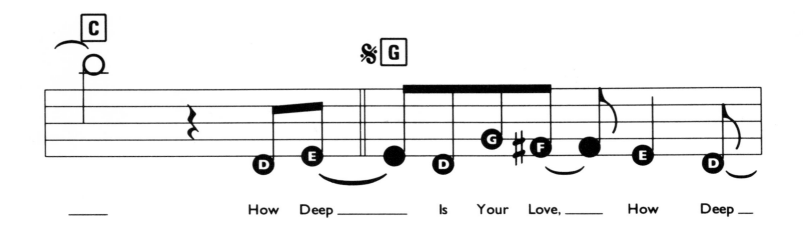

_____ How Deep _____ Is Your Love, _____ How Deep _____

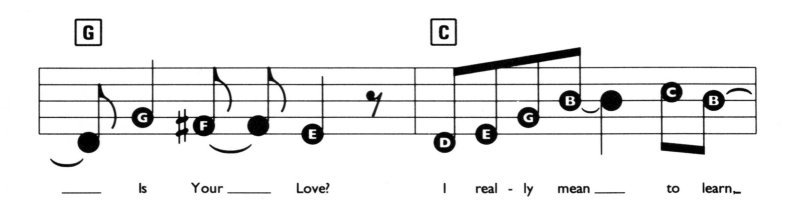

_____ Is Your _____ Love? I real - ly mean _____ to learn,

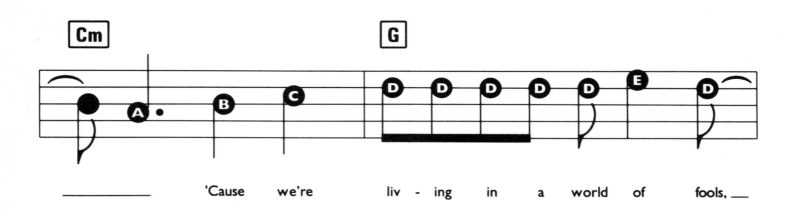

_____ 'Cause we're liv - ing in a world of fools, _____

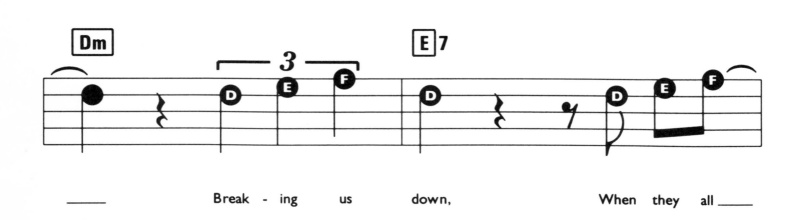

_____ Break - ing us down, When they all _____

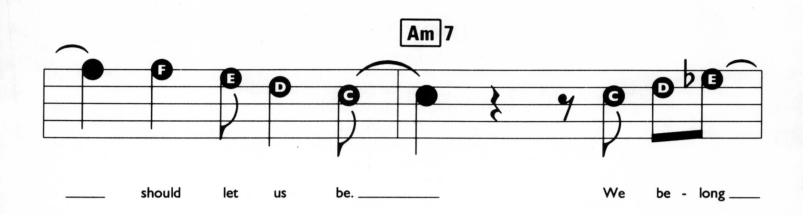

should   let   us   be. _____   We   be - long ____

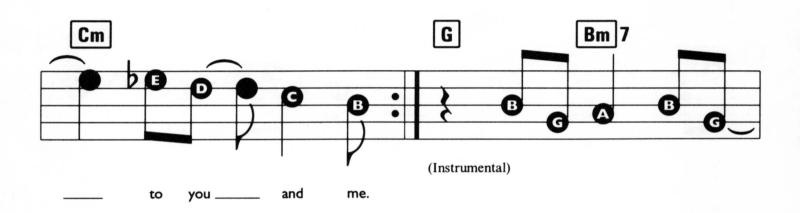

(Instrumental)

_____   to   you _____   and   me.

How   Deep ___

It's Impossible (Somos Novios)

Words by Sid Wayne
Music by A. Manzanero
© Copyright 1968 & 1970 by Editorial RCA Victor, SA Mexico.
All rights for the British Isles and Commonwealth (excluding Canada & Australasia)
controlled by BMG Music Publishing Limited, Bedford House, 69-79 Fulham High Street, London SW6.
This arrangement © Copyright 1995 BMG Music Publishing Limited.
All Rights Reserved. International Copyright Secured.

Registration: Flute or Strings
Rhythm: Swing (Ballad)
Tempo: Medium Slow

Trans 5

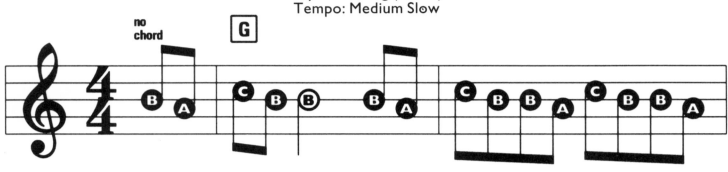

It's Im - poss - i - ble,   Tell the   sun to leave the sky, It's just im -

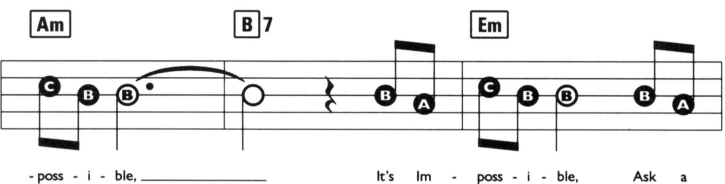

- poss - i - ble, _____   It's Im - poss - i - ble,   Ask a

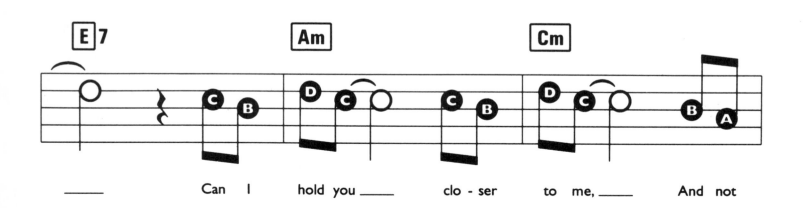

ba - by not to cry, It's just im - poss - i - ble. _____

_____ Can I hold you _____ clo - ser to me, _____ And not

14

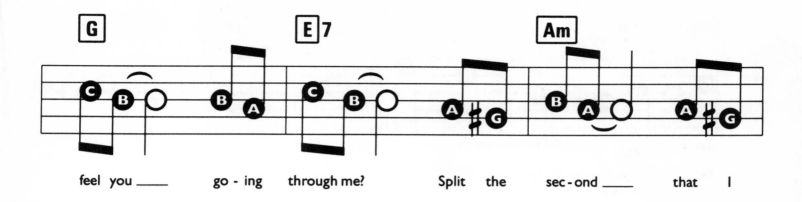

feel you _____ go - ing through me? Split the sec - ond _____ that I

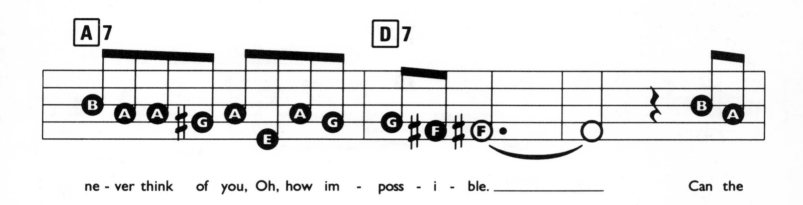

ne - ver think of you, Oh, how im - poss - i - ble. _____ Can the

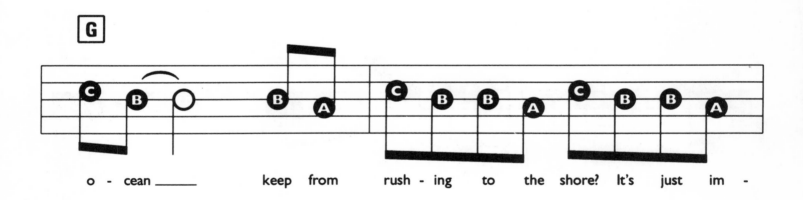

o - cean _____ keep from rush - ing to the shore? It's just im -

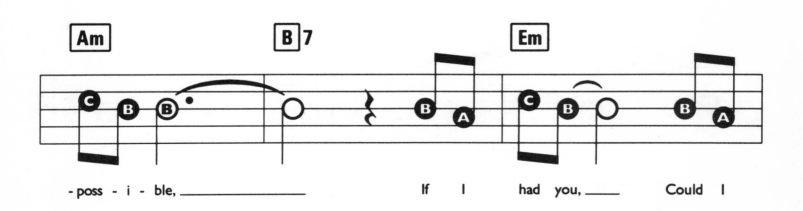

- poss - i - ble, _____ If I had you, _____ Could I

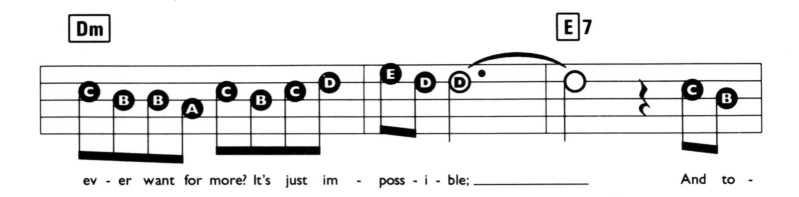

ev - er want for more? It's just im - poss - i - ble; _____ And to -

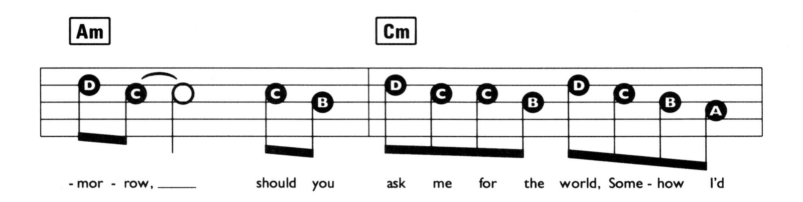

- mor - row, _____ should you ask me for the world, Some - how I'd

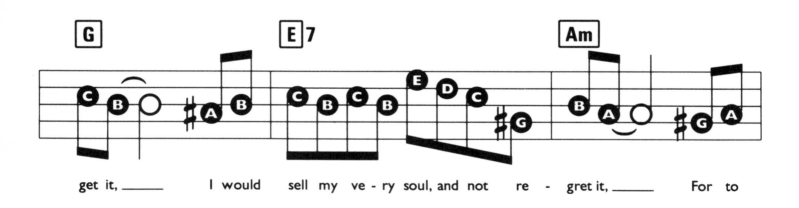

get it, _____ I would sell my ve - ry soul, and not re - gret it, _____ For to

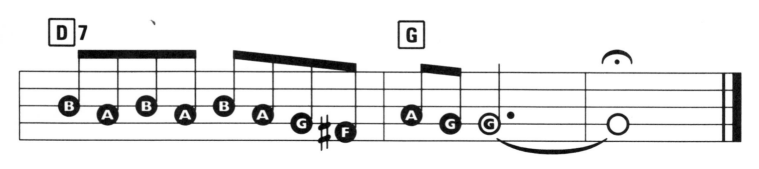

live with - out your love is just im - poss - i - ble. _____

I Write The Songs

Words & Music by Bruce Johnston

Registration: Saxophone or Piano
Rhythm: Soft Rock
Tempo: Medium

I've been a - live for ev - er,
My home lies deep with - in you,

And I wrote the ve - ry first _____ song.
And I have my own room in your soul.

I put the words and the me - lo - dies to - ge - ther, I'm
We're such good friends when I look out through your win - dows, I'm

mu - sic! And I Write The Songs.
young a - gain, though I'm ve - ry old.

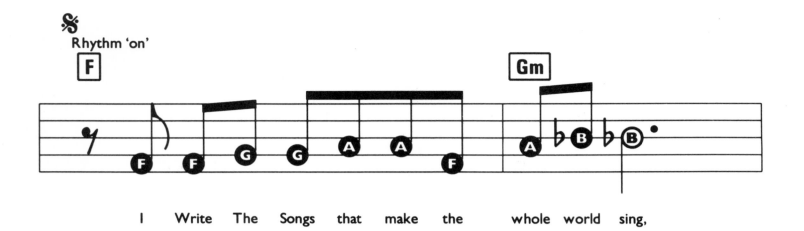

I Write The Songs that make the whole world sing,

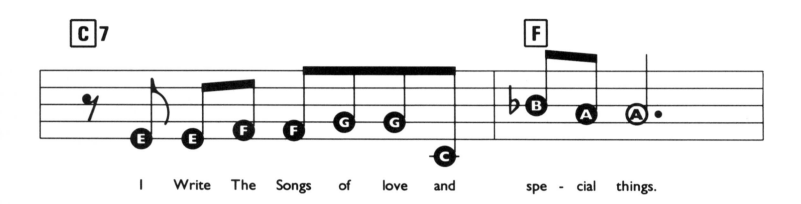

I Write The Songs of love and spe - cial things.

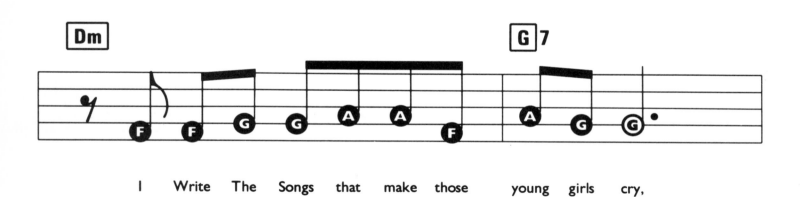

I Write The Songs that make those young girls cry,

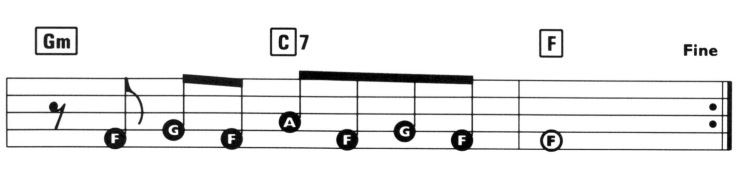

I Write The Songs, I Write The Songs.

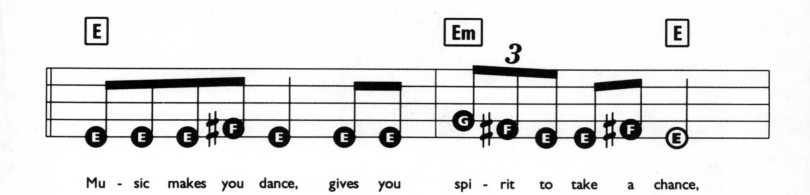

Mu - sic makes you dance, gives you spi - rit to take a chance,

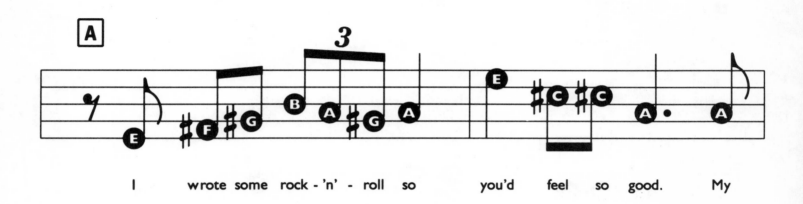

I wrote some rock - 'n' - roll so you'd feel so good. My

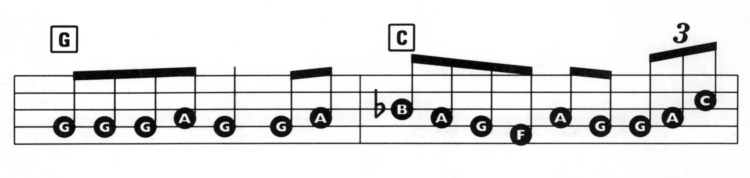

mu - sic's in your heart, It's a real fine place to start, ____ It's from me,

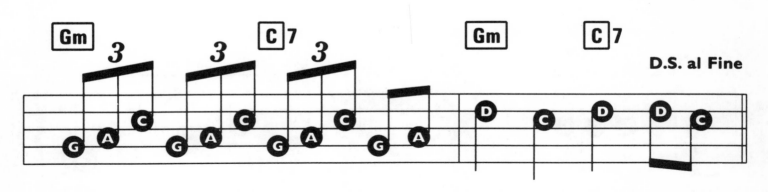

D.S. al Fine

It's thru' you, It's from you, It's thru' me, It's a world wide sym - pho - ny.

Jambalaya (On The Bayou)

Words & Music by Hank Williams
© Copyright 1952 renewed 1980 Hiriam Music & Acuff-Rose Music Incorporated, USA.
Acuff-Rose Music Limited, London W1.

Registration: Guitar or Trombone
Rhythm: Swing
Tempo: Medium

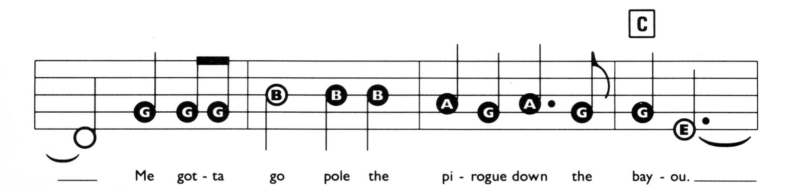

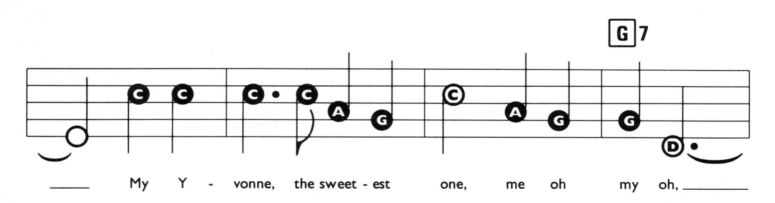

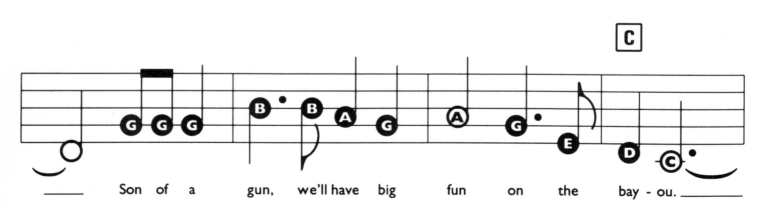

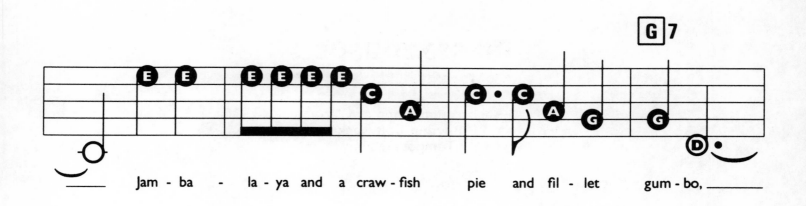

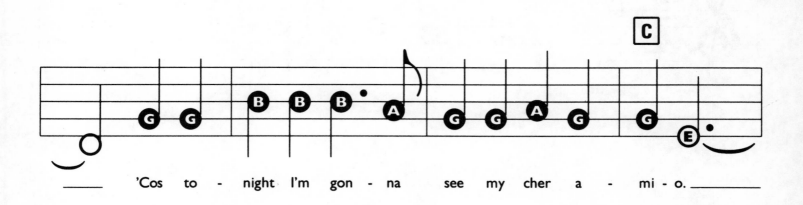

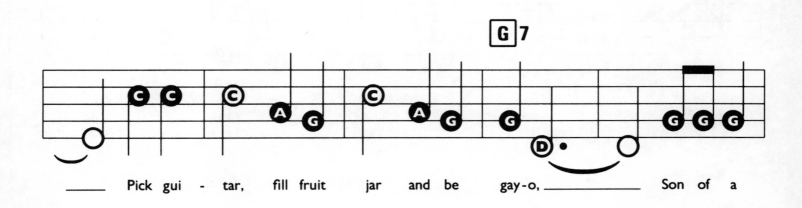

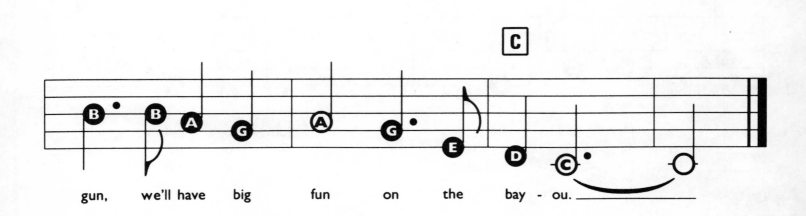

Massachusetts

Words & Music by Barry Gibb, Robin Gibb & Maurice Gibb

Registration: Piano or Clarinet
Rhythm: Soft Rock
Tempo: Medium

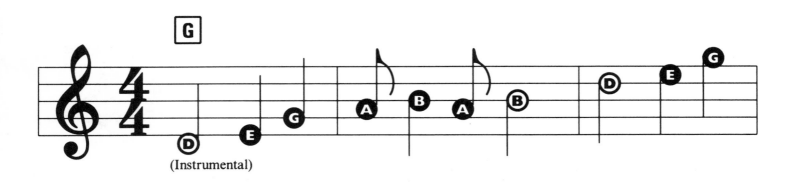

(Instrumental)

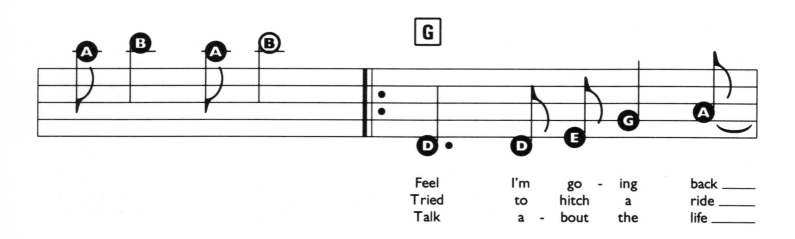

Feel	I'm	go -	ing	back ____
Tried	to	hitch	a	ride ____
Talk	a -	bout	the	life ____

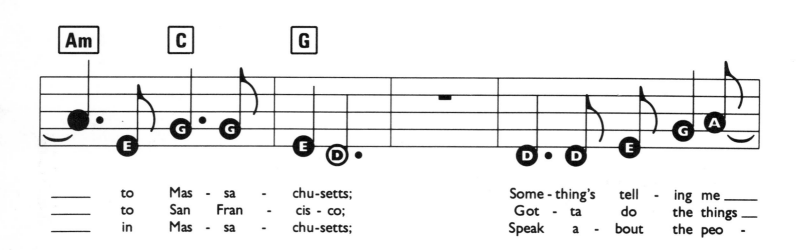

____	to	Mas - sa -	chu-setts;	Some - thing's	tell -	ing	me ____
____	to	San Fran -	cis - co;	Got -	ta	do	the things ____
____	in	Mas - sa -	chu-setts;	Speak	a -	bout	the peo -

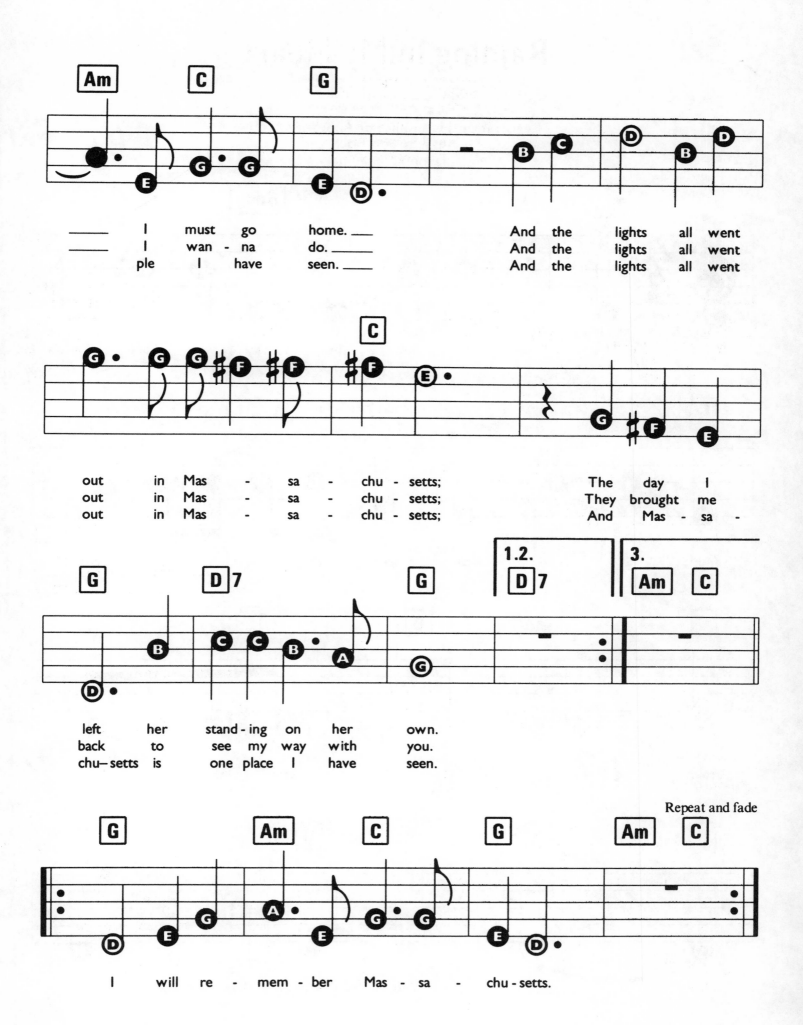

Raining In My Heart

Words & Music by Boudleaux & Felice Bryant

Registration: Harmonica or Acoustic Guitar
Rhythm: Soft Rock
Tempo: Medium

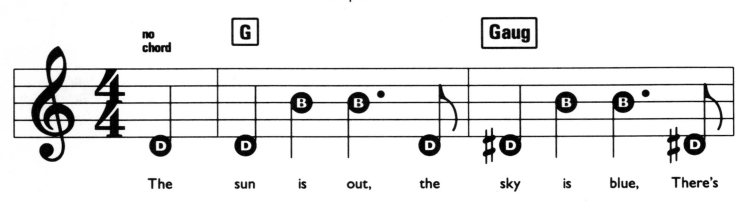

The sun is out, the sky is blue, There's

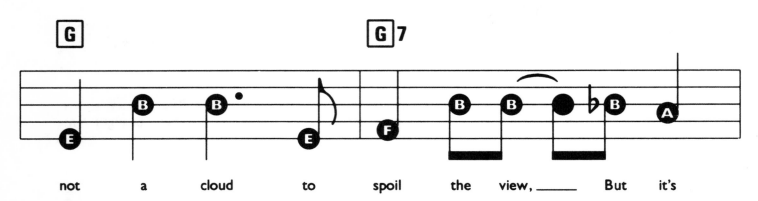

not a cloud to spoil the view, _____ But it's

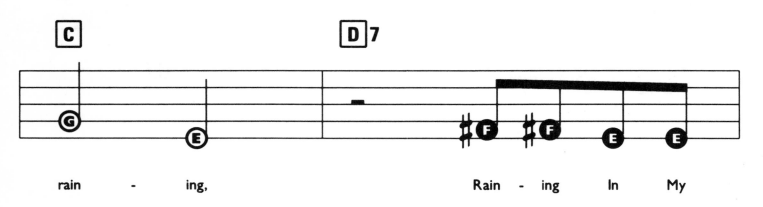

rain - ing, Rain - ing In My

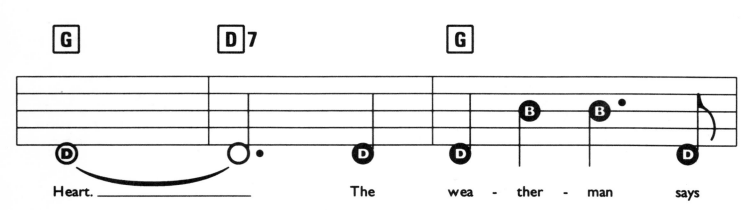

Heart. _____ The wea - ther - man says

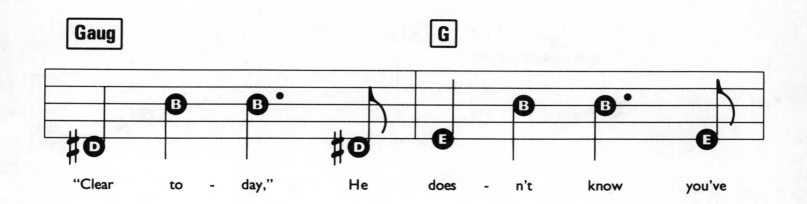

"Clear to - day," He does - n't know you've

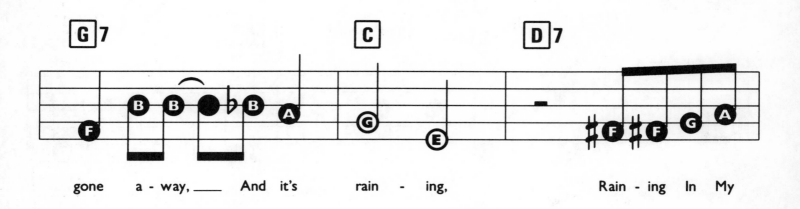

gone a - way, ___ And it's rain - ing, Rain - ing In My

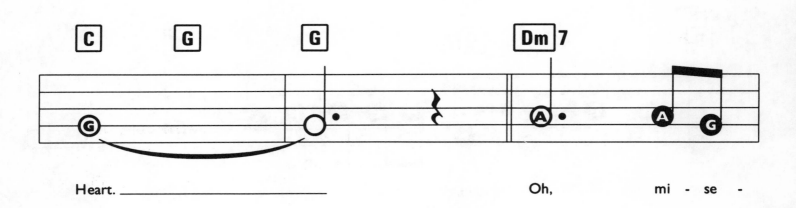

Heart. ___ Oh, mi - se -

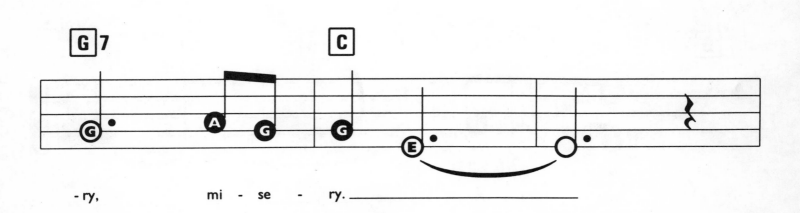

- ry, mi - se - ry. ___

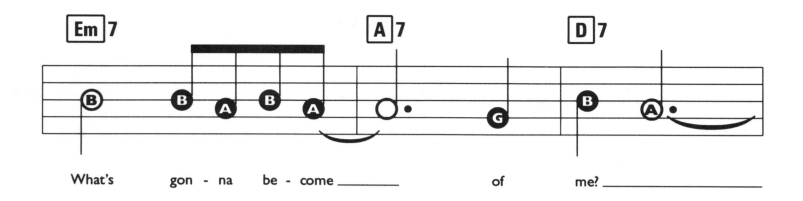

What's gon - na be - come _____ of me? _____

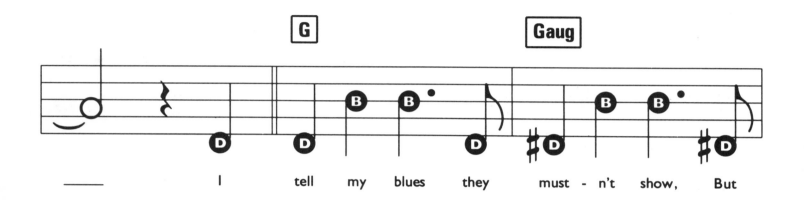

_____ I tell my blues they must - n't show, But

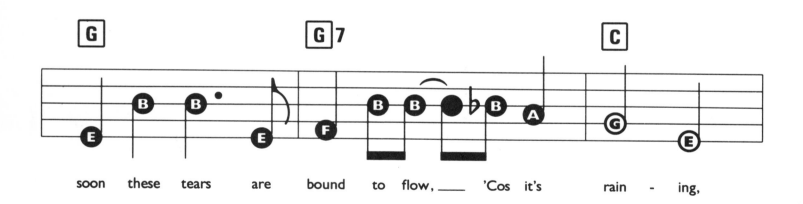

soon these tears are bound to flow, ____ 'Cos it's rain - ing,

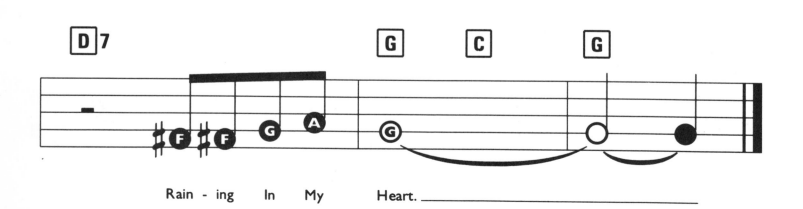

Rain - ing In My Heart. _____

Portrait Of My Love

Words by David West
Music by Cyril Ornadel

Registration: Saxophone or Strings
Rhythm: Swing (Ballad)
Tempo: Medium

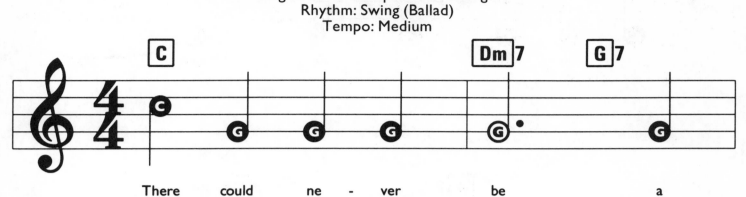

There could ne - ver be a

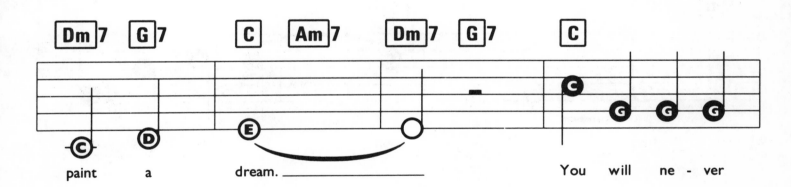

Por - trait Of My Love, For no - bo - dy could

paint a dream. You will ne - ver

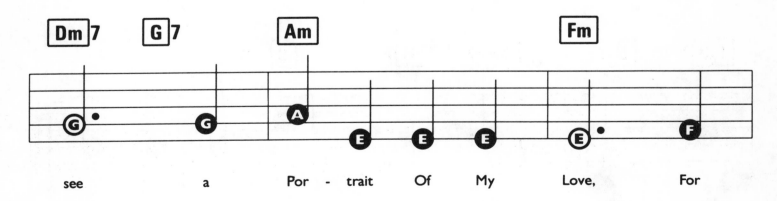

see a Por - trait Of My Love, For

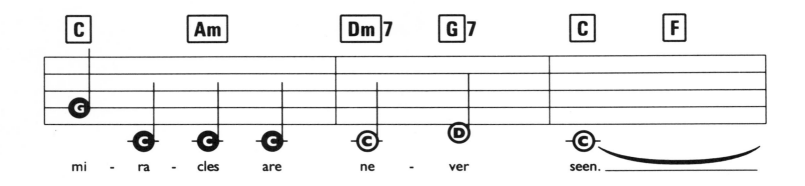

mi - ra - cles are ne - ver seen. _____

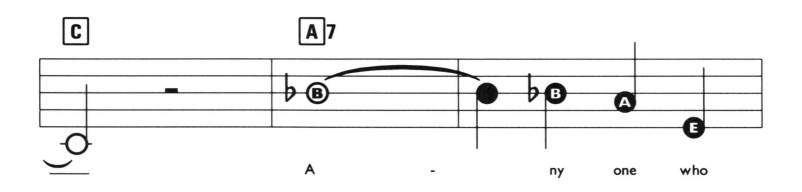

A - ny one who

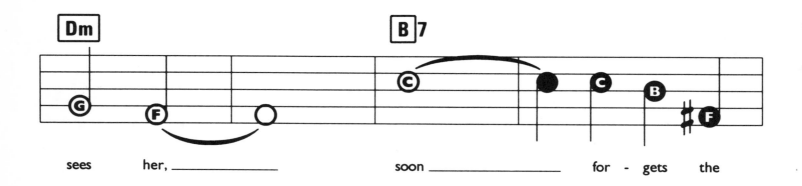

sees her, _____ soon _____ for - gets the

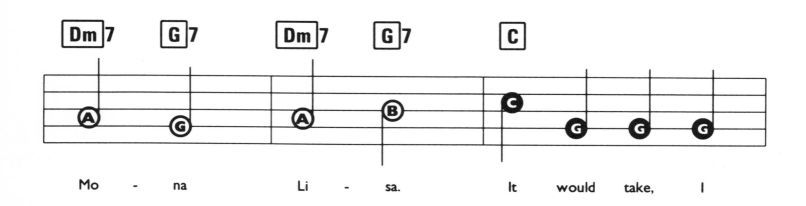

Mo - na Li - sa. It would take, I

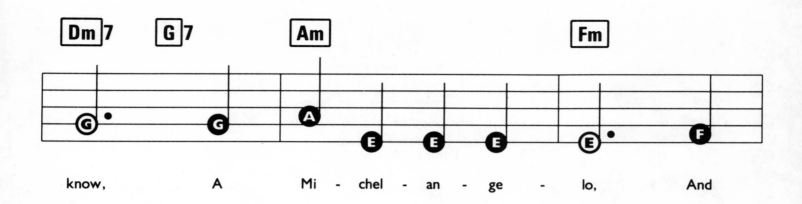

know, A Mi - chel - an - ge - lo, And

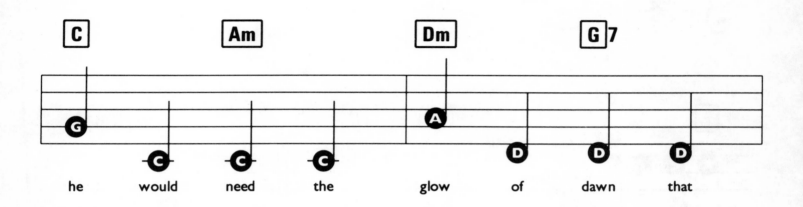

he would need the glow of dawn that

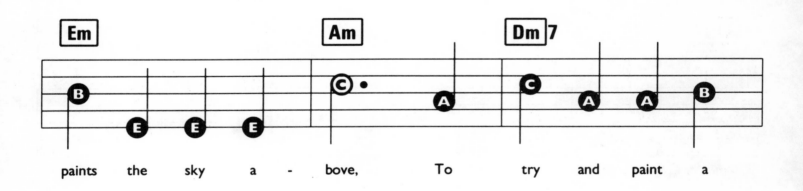

paints the sky a - bove, To try and paint a

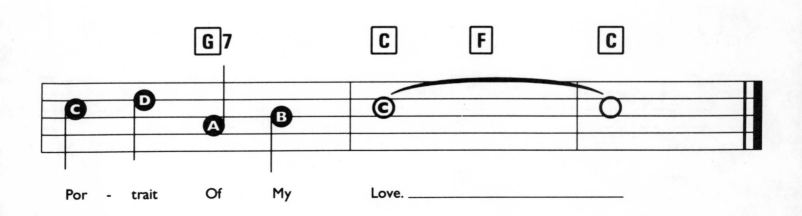

Por - trait Of My Love. _____

Sing

Words & Music by Joe Raposo

Registration: Vibraphone or Strings
Rhythm: Swing
Tempo: Medium Fast

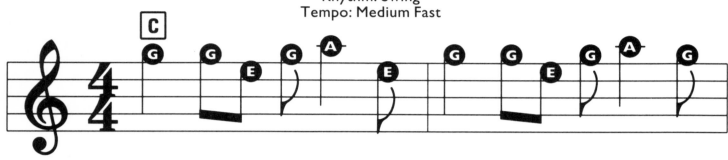

La   la   do   la   da,   La   da   la   do   la   da,   La

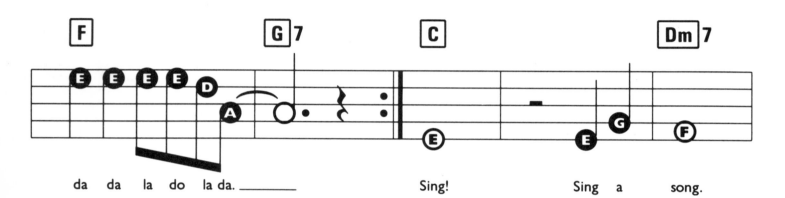

da   da   la   do   la   da. _____   Sing!   Sing   a   song.

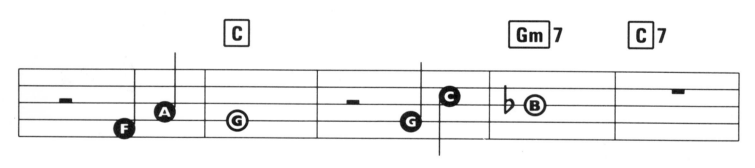

Sing   out   loud,   sing   out   strong.

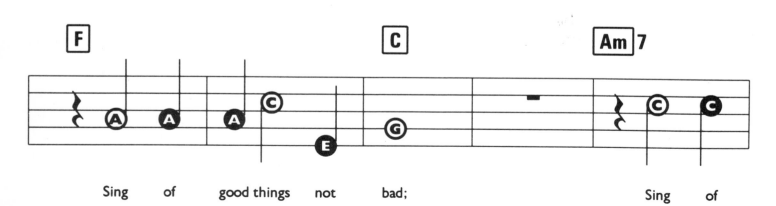

Sing   of   good things   not   bad;   Sing   of

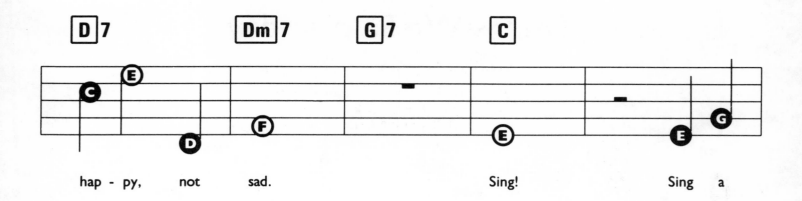

hap - py,   not   sad.   Sing!   Sing a

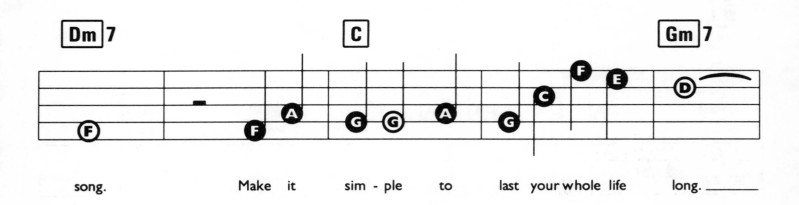

song.   Make   it   sim - ple   to   last your whole life   long. _____

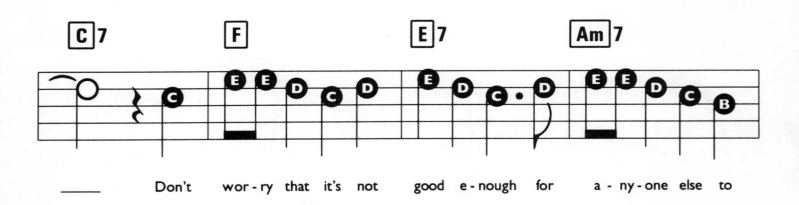

_____   Don't   wor - ry that   it's   not   good e - nough   for   a - ny - one else to

D.C. and fade

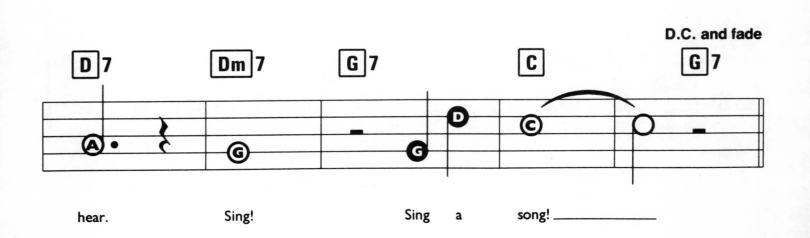

hear.   Sing!   Sing   a   song! _____

31

Things We Said Today

Words & Music by John Lennon & Paul McCartney
© Copyright 1964 Northern Songs.
All Rights Reserved. International Copyright Secured.

Registration: Trumpet or Rock Guitar
Rhythm: Rock
Tempo: Medium

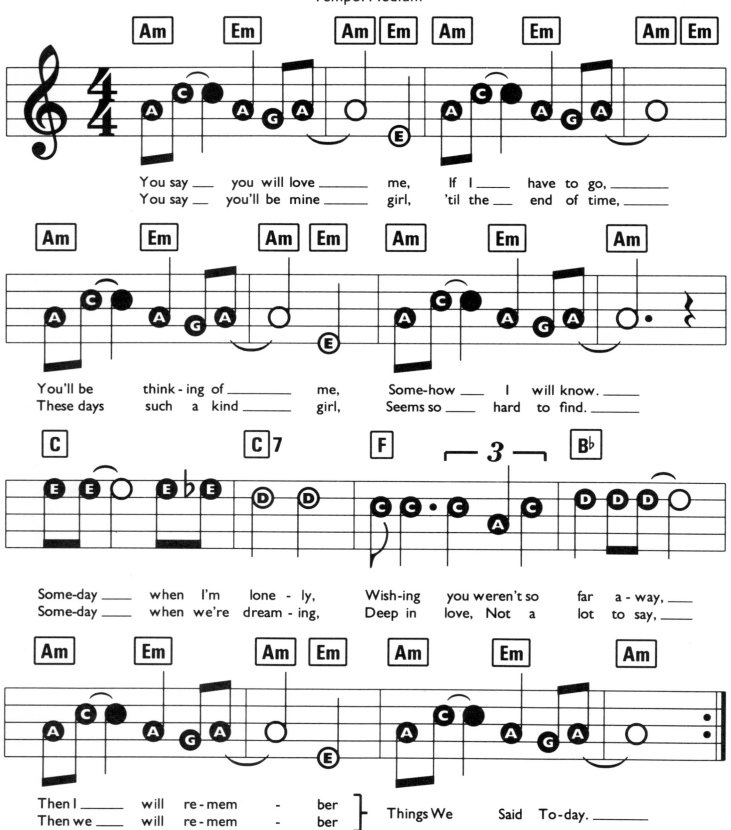

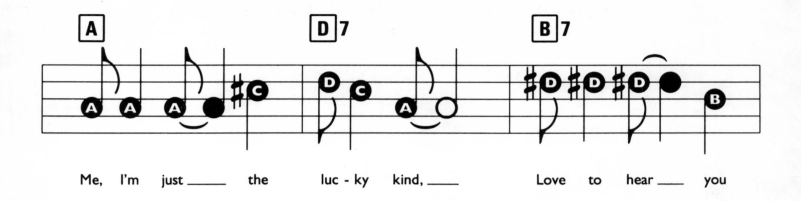

Me, I'm just ____ the luc - ky kind, ____ Love to hear ____ you

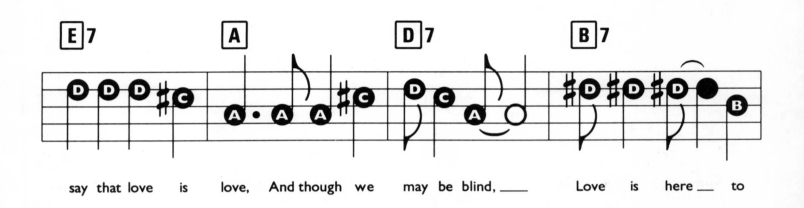

say that love is love, And though we may be blind, ____ Love is here ___ to

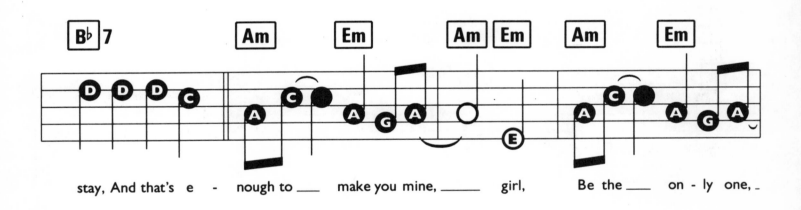

stay, And that's e - nough to ____ make you mine, _____ girl, Be the ___ on - ly one, _

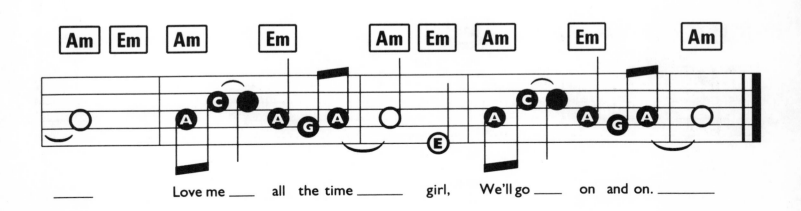

____ Love me ____ all the time _____ girl, We'll go ___ on and on. _____

This Guy's In Love With You

Words by Hal David
Music by Burt Bacharach

Registration: Piano or Trumpet
Rhythm: Swing
Tempo: Medium

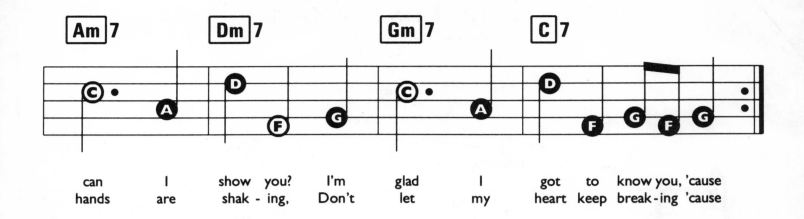

can   I   show you?   I'm   glad   I   got to   know you, 'cause
hands   are   shak - ing, Don't let   my   heart keep break-ing 'cause

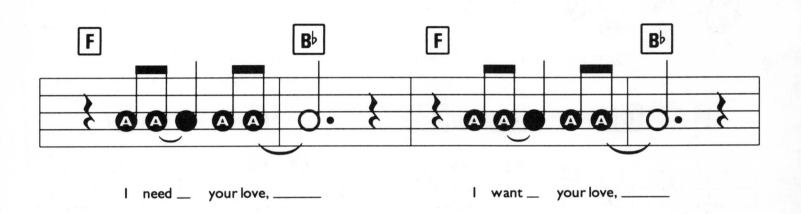

I need — your love, ———   I want — your love, ———

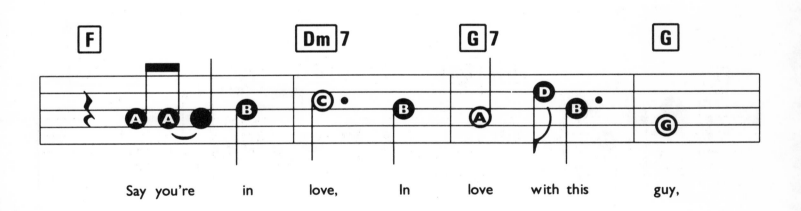

Say you're   in   love,   In   love with this   guy,

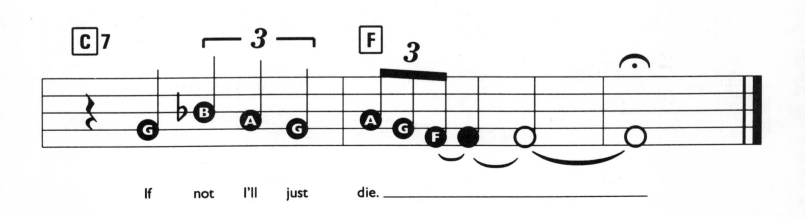

If   not   I'll   just   die. ————

True Love Ways

Words & Music by Buddy Holly & Norman Petty

Registration: Saxophone or Strings
Rhythm: Soft Rock
Tempo: Medium

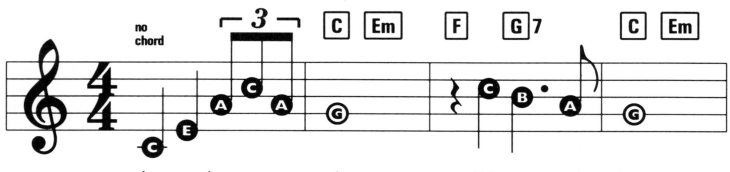

Just you know _____ why, Why you and I,

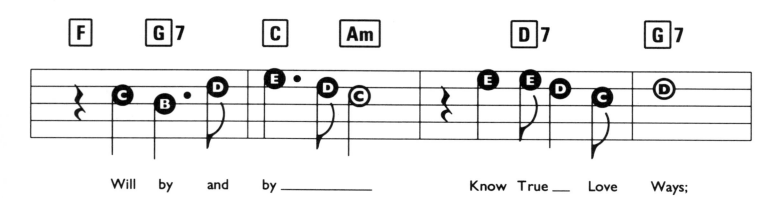

Will by and by _____ Know True _ Love Ways;

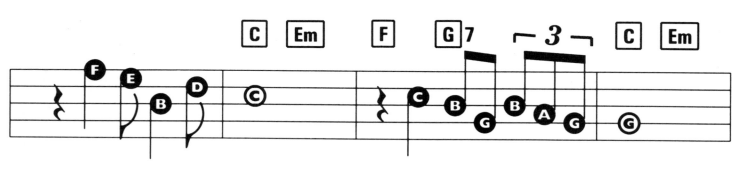

Some-times _ we'll sigh, Some-times _____ we'll cry,

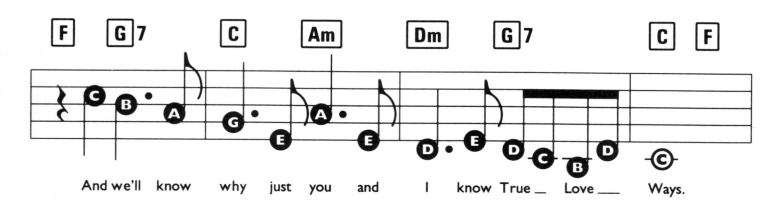

And we'll know why just you and I know True _ Love _ Ways.

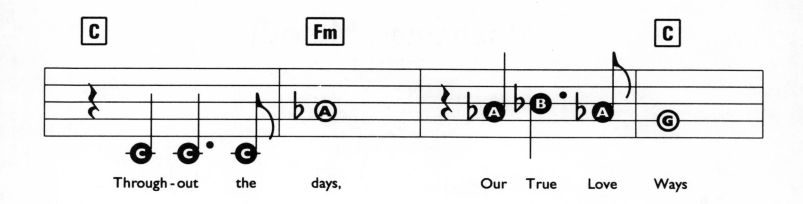

Through - out the days, Our True Love Ways

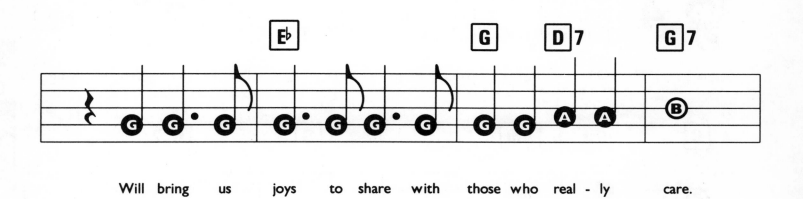

Will bring us joys to share with those who real - ly care.

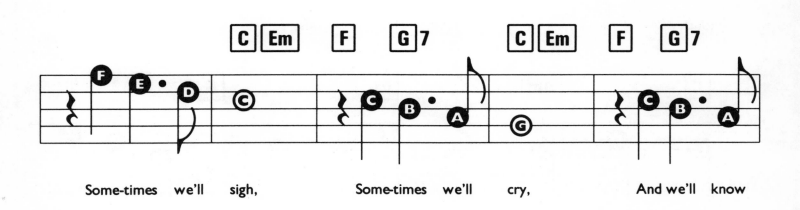

Some-times we'll sigh, Some-times we'll cry, And we'll know

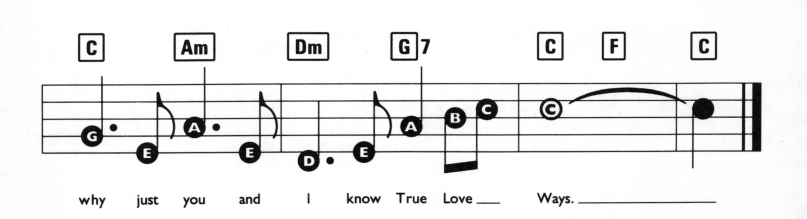

why just you and I know True Love ___ Ways. _____

Unchained Melody

Music by Alex North
Words by Hy Zaret

Registration: Flute or Strings
Rhythm: Swing (Ballad)
Tempo: Medium Slow

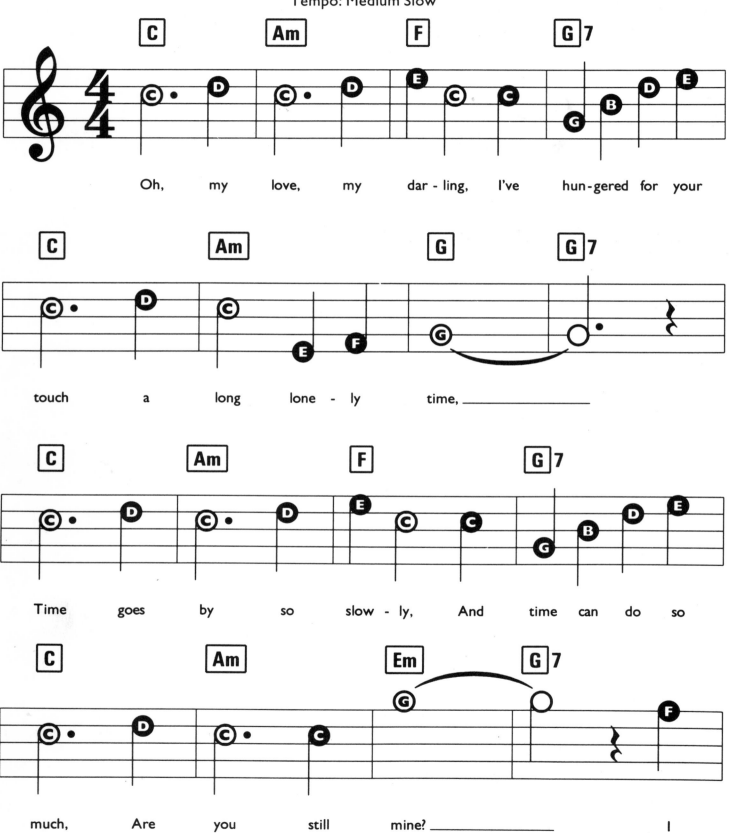

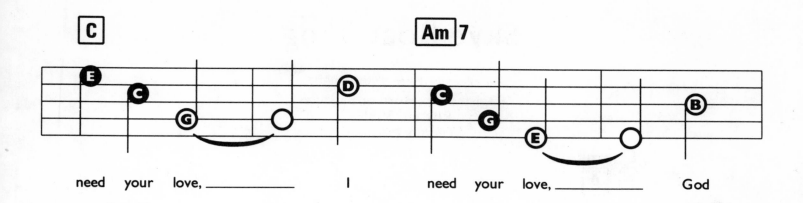

need your love, _____ I need your love, _____ God

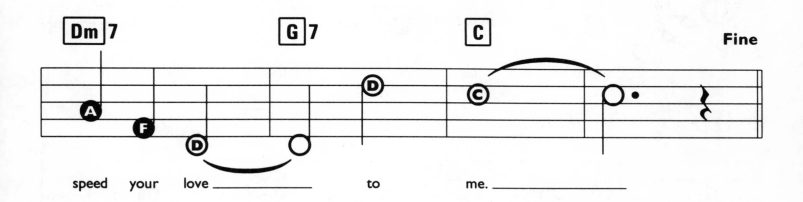

speed your love _____ to me. _____

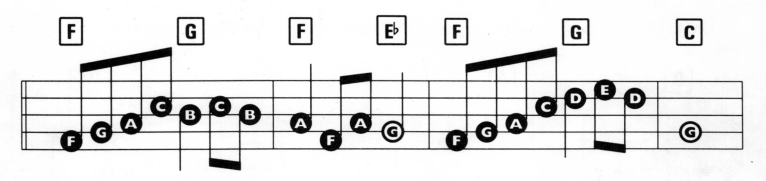

Lone-ly ri-vers flow to the sea, To the sea, To the o-pen arms of the sea,

D.C. al Fine

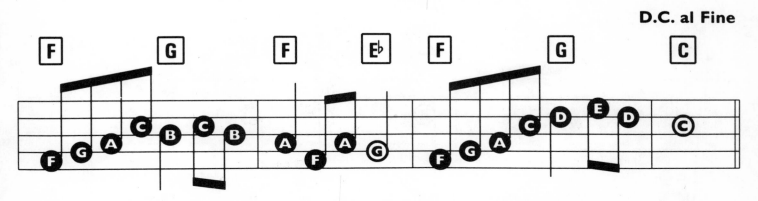

Lone-ly ri-vers sigh "Wait for me, Wait for me," I'll be com-ing home, Wait for me.

39

Skye Boat Song

Traditional

Registration: Horn or Bagpipes
Rhythm: Waltz
Tempo: Medium

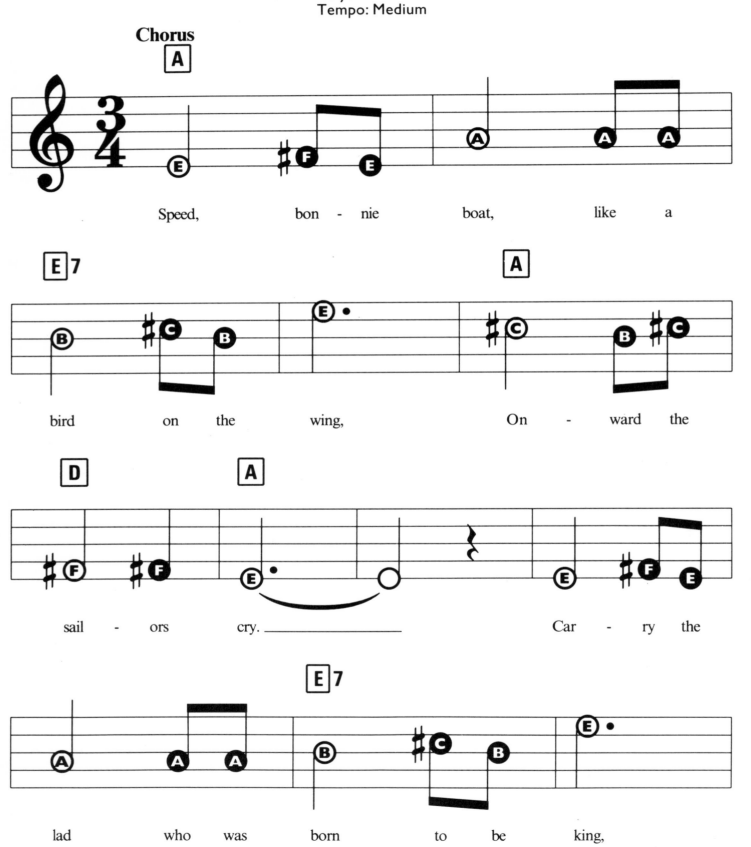

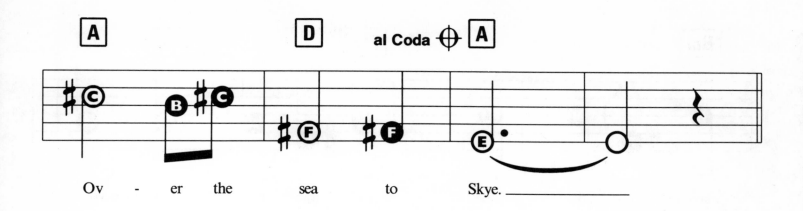

Ov - er the sea to Skye. _____

Verse

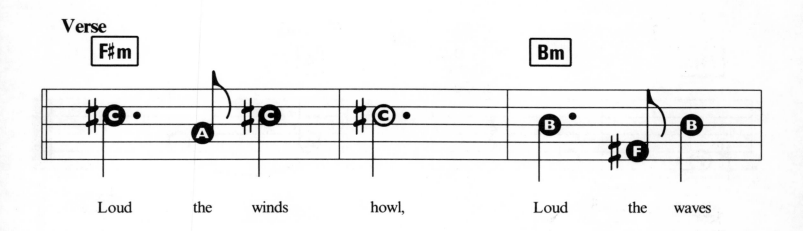

Loud the winds howl, Loud the waves

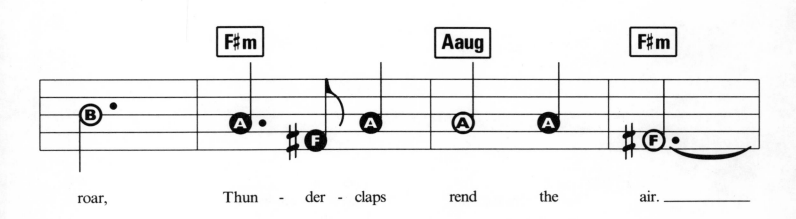

roar, Thun - der - claps rend the air. _____

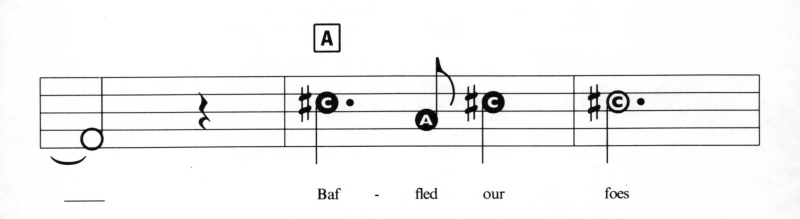

_____ Baf - fled our foes

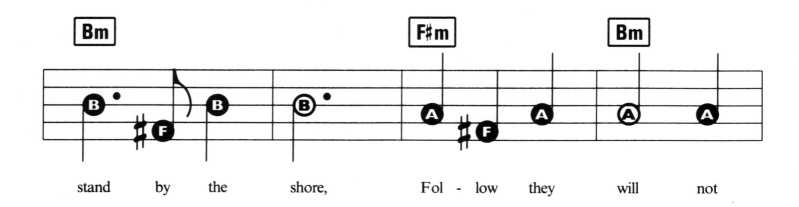

stand   by   the   shore,   Fol - low   they   will   not

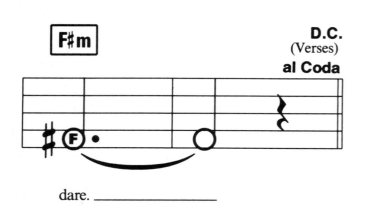

dare. _____

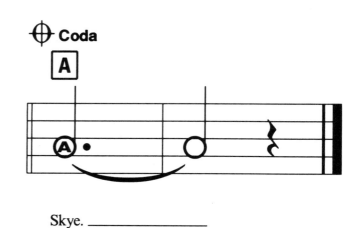

Skye. _____

Verse 2
Though the waves leap,
Soft shall ye sleep
Ocean's a royal bed.
Rocked in the deep,
Flora will keep
Watch by your weary head.

(Chorus)

Verse 3
Burned are our homes,
Exile and death,
Scatter the loyal men.
Yet ere the sword
Cool in the sheath,
Charlie will come again.

(Chorus)

Way Of The World

Words & Music by Graham Lyle & Albert Hammond

Registration: Saxophone or Vibraphone
Rhythm: Soft Rock
Tempo: Medium Slow

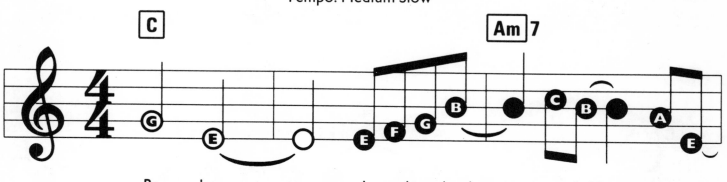

Ba - by, _____ I need a hand _____ to hold _____ to - night, _

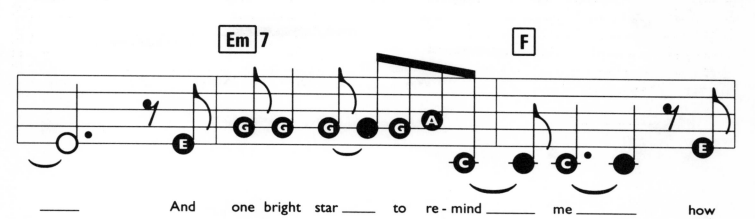

_____ And one bright star _____ to re - mind _____ me _____ how

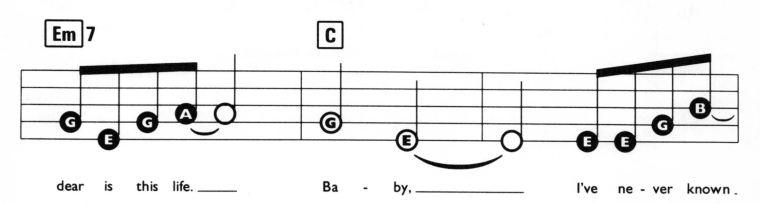

dear is this life. _____ Ba - by, _____ I've ne - ver known _

_____ a - ny - one like you, _____ There's some - thing ve - ry spe - cial a - bout _

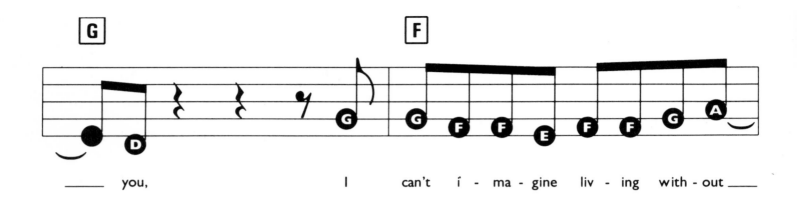

_____ you,   I   can't í - ma - gine liv - ing with - out _____

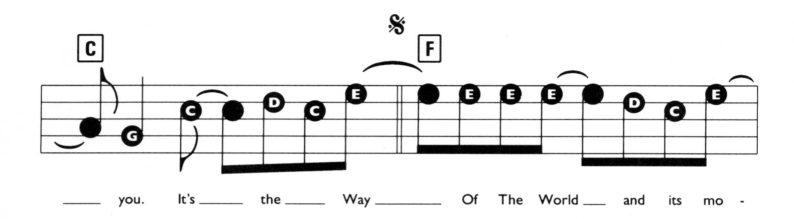

_____ you.   It's _____ the _____ Way _____ Of The World _____ and   its   mo -

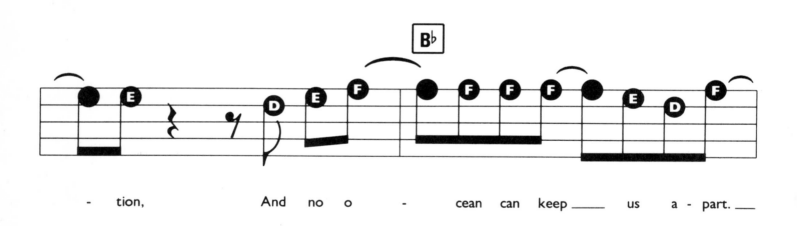

- tion,   And no   o -   cean can keep _____ us   a - part. ___

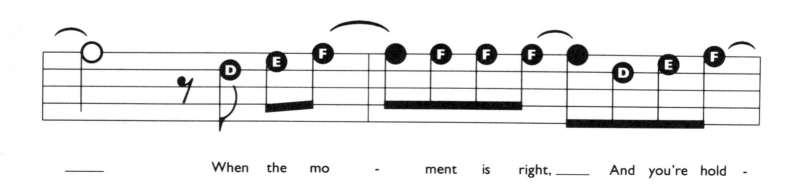

_____   When the mo -   ment is right, _____ And you're hold -

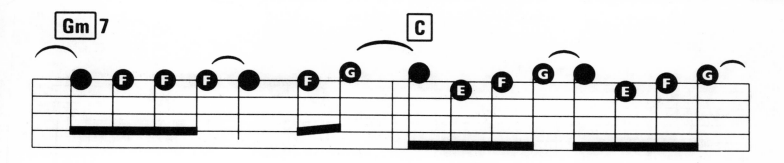

- ing me tight, _____ You cap - ture the beat _____ of my heart. __

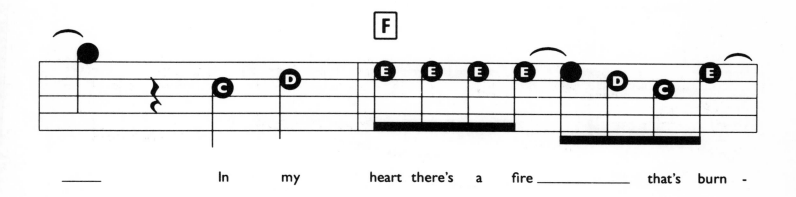

_____ In my heart there's a fire _____ that's burn -

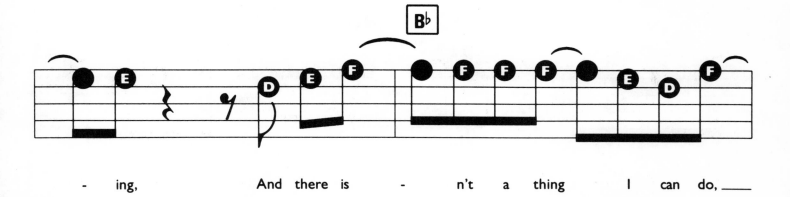

- ing, And there is - n't a thing I can do, _____

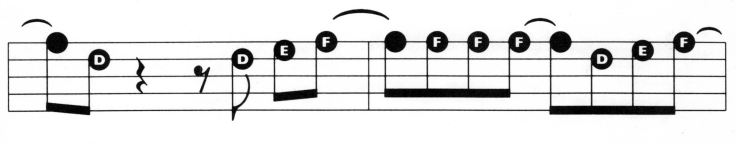

_____ I'm re - signed _____ to the fact _____ that there's no _____

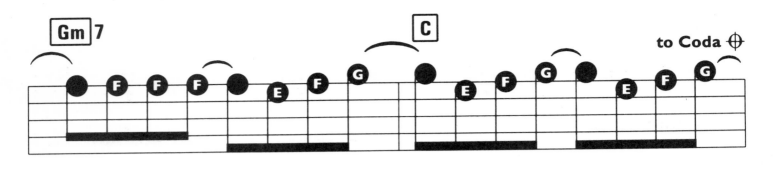

turn - ing back, ___ And I'll ne - ver re - gret ___ lov - ing you. ___

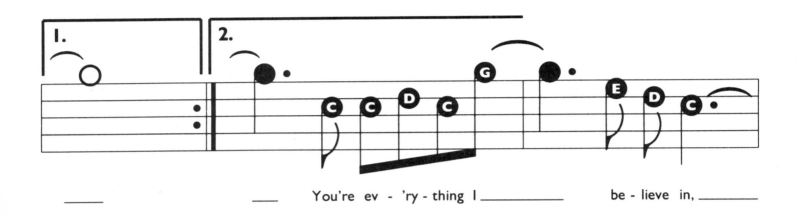

___ ___ You're ev - 'ry - thing I _____ be - lieve in, ___

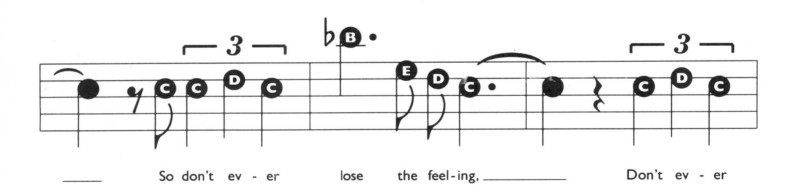

___ So don't ev - er lose the feel - ing, _____ Don't ev - er

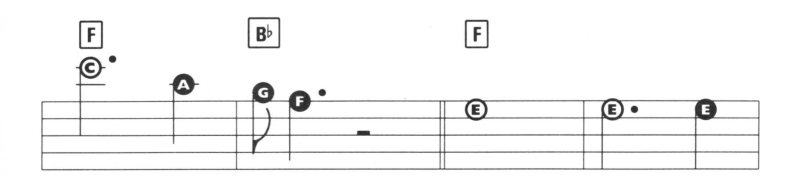

lose the feel - ing. (Instrumental)

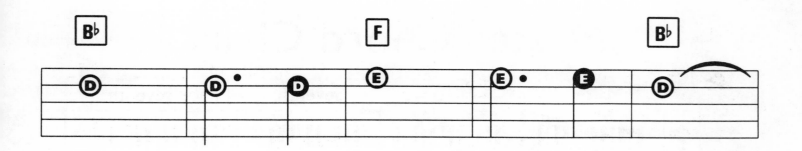

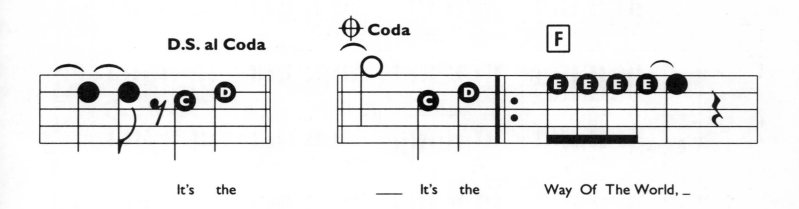

It's   the   It's   the   Way Of The World,

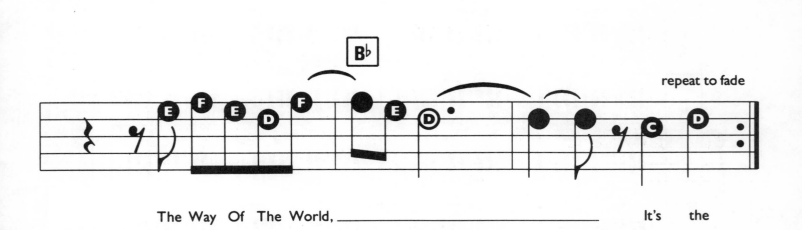

The Way Of The World, _____   It's   the

2.   Baby, I will go anywhere you lead,
           As long as you're there beside me,
           Baby that's all I need,
           Hold me, hold me and never let me go,
           I'm always gonna care about you,
           I never wanna be without you.

Master Chord Chart

	Major	Minor	Seventh	Minor seventh
C				
C#/Db				
D				
Eb				
E				
F				
F#/Gb				
G				
Ab				
A				
Bb				
B				

Diminished Chords.

C dim Eb dim F#/Gb dim A dim   C#/Db dim E dim G dim Bb dim   D dim F dim Ab dim B dim

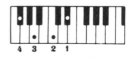

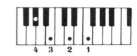

Augmented Chords

C aug E aug Ab aug   C#/Db aug F aug A aug   D aug F#/Gb aug Bb aug   Eb aug G aug B aug

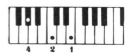